GREAT BRITISH THINGS TO MAKE AND DO

SAMANTHA MEREDITH
SALLY MORGAN

SCHOLASTIC

Scholastic Children's Books,
Euston House, 24 Eversholt Street,
London NW1 1DB, UK

A division of Scholastic Ltd
London ~ New York ~ Toronto ~ Sydney ~ Auckland
Mexico City ~ New Delhi ~ Hong Kong

Editor: Corinne Lucas

Published in the UK by Scholastic Ltd, 2014

Illustrated by Samantha Meredith
Text by Sally Morgan
© Scholastic Children's Books, 2014

ISBN 978 1407 13962 3

Printed in Malaysia.

2 4 6 8 10 9 7 5 3 1

Papers used by Scholastic Children's Books are made from woods grown
in sustainable forests.

GREAT BRITISH SPOT THE DIFFERENCE

Can you spot ten differences between these pictures? You can find out how to make some of the items in these pictures throughout the book.

ST DAVID'S DAY

Celebrate St David's Day, the patron saint of Wales, on March 1st by making your own daffodil button-hole to wear.

You will need

- a cardboard egg box
- scissors
- paper
- a sharp pencil
- card
- a paintbrush
- yellow paint
- modelling clay
- a green pipe cleaner
- sticky tape
- a glue stick
- a safety pin.

1. Cut off one of the egg cups from the cardboard egg box. Trim around the top with scissors to neaten the edges.

2. Trace over the flower and circle templates on the opposite page using a pencil and piece of paper and cut them out.

3. Draw around your templates on a piece of card and cut them out.

4. Paint the cup from your egg box, the cardboard flower and the circle yellow and leave them to dry.

5. Ask an adult to place the egg cup on the piece of modelling clay and make a hole in the centre by pushing a sharp pencil through the middle into the clay. Repeat this to make a hole in the centre of your flower.

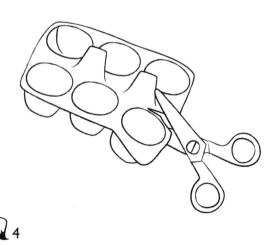

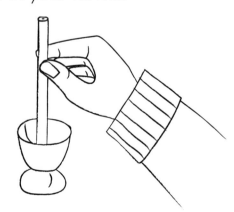

6. Push the end of the pipe cleaner through the hole in the flower and then through the hole in the egg cup, from the outside. Fold over 2 cm of pipe cleaner inside the cup and secure with sticky tape. Bend the pipe cleaner so your daffodil is facing forwards.

7. Apply glue to the back of the yellow circle and stick it in the centre of the egg cup to cover the end of the pipe cleaner. Leave it to dry.

8. Pin your daffodil to your chest and wear it with pride.

LOVELY LOVE SPOONS

In Wales, it's tradition to give people love spoons to celebrate weddings and anniversaries. Can you decorate and colour these love spoons?

PERFECT PANCAKES

Celebrate Shrove Tuesday by whipping up a batch of home-made pancakes.

You will need
- 225 g plain flour
- 2 eggs, beaten
- 600 ml milk
- knob of butter
- salt.

1. Sift the flour into a large bowl, add a pinch of salt and stir.

2. Pour in the beaten eggs and whisk the mixture until there are no lumps.

3. Slowly pour in the milk and stir. Cover the bowl and leave the mixture to stand for 30 minutes.

4. Ask an adult to put a non-stick frying pan over a high heat. Add the butter and let it melt.

> **Warning!** *Make sure you ask an adult to help you whenever you'd like to use the hob.*

5. Spoon some of your mixture into the pan and swirl the pan around until the base is covered in pancake batter.

6. When the top of the batter has set, shake the pan to loosen your pancake and flip it over to cook the other side for one minute.

7. Tip onto a plate and add a topping of your choice.

Great British tip
Pancakes taste best smothered in fresh lemon juice and sugar.

I-SPY ENGLAND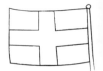

How many of these famous English things can you spy when you are out and about in England?

English flag ○

Double-decker bus ○

Cornish pasty ○

Thatched cottage ○

Red rose ○

Game of cricket ○

Red post box ○

Morris dancer ○

Red phone box ○

Black taxi cab ○

Beefeater ○

Underground station ○

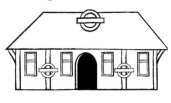

Strawberries and cream ○

Oak tree ○

Lion statue ○

 # CORNISH PASTY

Make these traditional Cornish savoury treats, perfect for a spring or summer picnic.

You will need

- 740 g ready-rolled shortcrust pastry
- 1 tbsp plain flour
- 400 g chuck steak, chopped
- 1 onion, chopped
- 1 large baking potato, chopped
- ½ swede, chopped
- 1 egg, beaten
- pinch of salt and pepper.

Warning! *Make sure you ask an adult to help you whenever you'd like to use a sharp knife or the oven.*

1. Ask an adult to preheat the oven to 200 °C/gas mark 6.

2. Put the steak, onion, potato, swede, salt and pepper into a large bowl and mix together.

3. Sprinkle flour on your work surface and place a sheet of pastry on top. Lay a small plate on top of your pastry and cut around it using a table knife.

4. Spoon the mixture on to the right-hand side of your pastry circles, leaving a 3 cm gap around the edge of the pastry for the crust.

5. Brush around the edge of each circle with egg. Fold the pastry in half to make a semi-circle. Press the edges together so no mixture leaks out.

6. Brush each of your pasties with egg to make them nice and shiny.

7. Place your pasties on a greased baking tray and ask an adult to put them in the oven for 15 minutes.

8. After 15 minutes, ask an adult to turn the oven down to 180 °C/gas mark 4 and bake for 40 minutes.

9. When the pasties are golden brown, leave to cool and enjoy.

9

MOTHERS' DAY MAGIC

Make your Mum feel extra-special this Mothers' Day by getting her to put her feet up and have home-made afternoon tea.

Afternoon tea stand

You will need
- 3 large paper plates
- 2 paper cups
- a sharp pencil
- a lump of modelling clay
- 150 cm gift ribbon
- sticky tape
- scissors.

1. Ask an adult to place a paper plate onto the piece of modelling clay and push a sharp pencil through the middle to make a hole. Repeat this for each of the paper plates and the paper cups.

2. Fold the ribbon in half and thread the folded part through the hole in the underside of a large plate. Secure the ends of ribbon with sticky tape to the bottom of the plate.

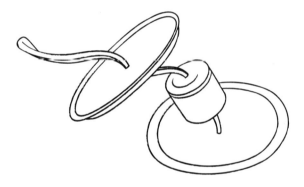

3. Continue to thread the ribbon from the top of the plate, through the hole in the cup and then through the underside of the other large paper plate. Repeat for the second cup and the last plate.

4. Cut the ribbon at the fold and tie with a knot.

To make finger sandwiches

You will need
- 150 g cream cheese
- 1 tbsp mayonnaise
- salt and pepper
- 3 slices wholemeal bread
- ½ cucumber, sliced
- 3 slices white bread.

1. Put the cream cheese, mayonnaise and a pinch of salt and pepper in a bowl and mix together.

2. Spread the mixture onto one side of each slice of wholemeal bread.

3. Lay the cucumber slices on top of the mixture.

4. Place the white slices of bread on top of the cucumber.

5. Cut the crusts off the sandwiches using a table knife. Cut each sandwich into four triangles.

6. Arrange on your afternoon tea stand, so that a brown side is next to a white side.

Great British tip
Serve your sandwiches with a pot of tea. Make your Mum feel extra special by adding some cakes to enjoy with your sandwiches.

11

ST GEORGE'S DAY

Celebrate St George's Day, on April 23rd, by putting on your very own St George and the dragon finger-puppet show.

You will need
- colouring pencils
- scissors.

1. Colour in the two puppets on the opposite page.

2. Turn the page over and colour in the other side.

3. Cut out your puppets using scissors. Take extra care when cutting out the circles for your fingers to go through.

4. Insert the index finger and middle finger on your right hand into the holes at the bottom of the dragon puppet. Do the same with your left hand with the holes in the St George puppet.

5. Put on a show! In the legend, George slays the dragon, but you can rewrite the story in any way that you like.

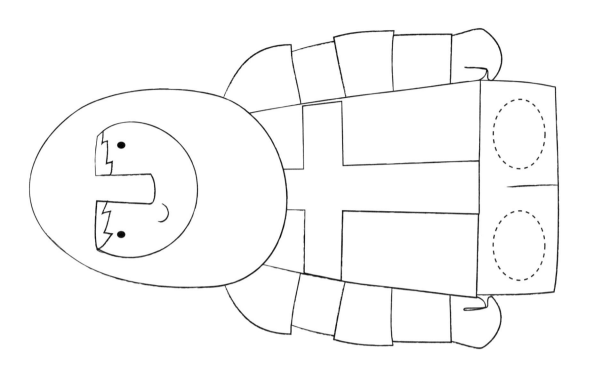

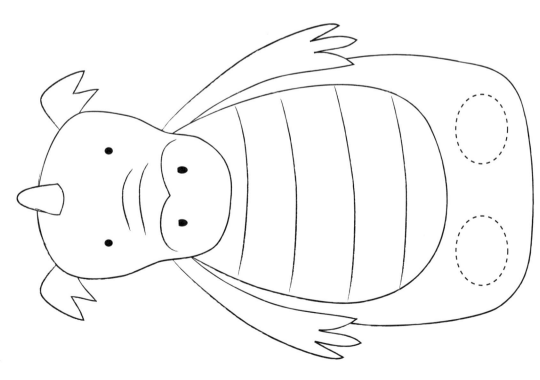

13

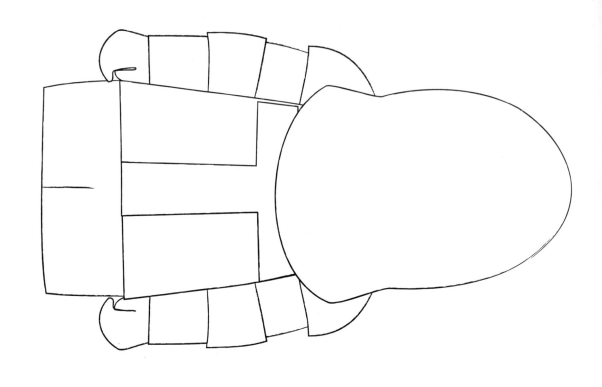

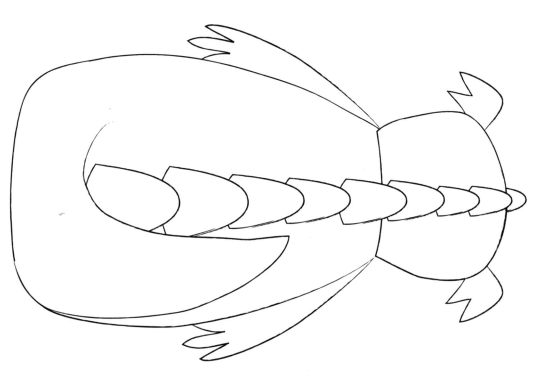

14

MUNRO MAYHEM

A mountain in Scotland higher 3,000 feet is called a Munro. Climbers from all over the world come to Scotland to try to climb them. Can you help these climbers reach the summit?

TURN AROUND

15

 # POOH STICKS

The game of pooh sticks is a Great British tradition. There's even a World Pooh Sticks Championships, held each year in Oxfordshire.

You will need
- a stick each
- a footbridge
- a stream.

1. Ask each player to find a stick and meet you on the footbridge.

2. Stand in the middle of the bridge and hold your sticks over the upstream side.

3. One player says 'Pooh', and everyone must drop, not throw, their sticks into the water.

4. Go to the other side of the bridge and wait for the sticks to appear.

5. The winner is the player whose stick is the first to come out from beneath the bridge.

Great British rule
Only use natural sticks. Any lollipop or plastic sticks thrown into the stream counts as littering and leads to instant disqualification!

SUMMER LASSI

When things get hot this summer, what better way to cool down than with a delicious, Indian-inspired mango lassi?

You will need

- 250 ml plain yoghurt
- 125 ml semi-skimmed milk
- 250 g fresh mangoes, chopped
- 125 ml mango juice
- sugar
- ice cubes
- tall glasses.

1. Place your glasses into the freezer to chill.

2. Put all of your ingredients, except the sugar and ice cubes, into a blender and ask an adult to blend it until all of the mango has broken up and mixed into the yoghurt and milk.

3. Have a taste of your lassi. Mangoes are very sweet, but if you think your drink could use more sweetness, add a little sugar and blend again.

4. Take your glasses out of the freezer and put a few ice cubes into the bottom of each one. Pour in your smooth summer lassi and enjoy with thirsty friends.

Great British tip
Why stop at mango? Experiment with any fruit that takes your fancy. Slurrrrp-tastic!

FUN AT THE FÊTE

Welly wanging, coconut shies, raffles – nothing is more fun than a British summer fête. Why not have your own?

Coconut shy

You will need
- 6 empty toilet rolls
- paint
- paintbrushes
- newspaper
- masking tape
- tennis balls.

1. Paint your toilet rolls in bold, bright colours and leave to dry.

2. Take a large sheet of newspaper and scrunch it up into a ball shape. Cover the outside of your ball in masking tape to hold it together. Repeat to make five balls.

3. Paint your newspaper balls with brown paint. Experiment with different shades to get a textured effect like the outside of a coconut. Leave to dry.

4. Stand your toilet rolls on their ends and line them up on a table or against a wall. Balance a paper coconut on the top of each toilet roll.

5. To play, each player takes it in turns to stand 3 metres away from the line of 'coconuts' and throws three tennis balls to try to knock over as many as they can.

Wang a Welly

You will need
- a stick
- a Wellington boot
- stones.

1. Lay the stick horizontally on the ground. Each player must stand behind this marker when they take their turn.

2. From behind the marker, each player must throw the Wellington boot as far as they can, three times.

3. Use the stones to mark where the Wellington boot lands.

4. The winner is the player who throws the welly furthest.

Ways to Wang
Try different throwing techniques to see what works best for you.

Backwards
Stand with your back to the marker, hold your welly in both hands, bend your knees and swing it between your legs, then up and over your head, and let go.

Underarm
Stand facing forwards, hold the welly out in front of you and then, keeping your arm straight, swing it back and then forward as quickly as you can and release the welly.

The Hammer Toss
Give the game a twist, by throwing your welly like the hammer in the Highland Games. Spin around on the spot, just behind the marker. When you are going really fast, and are facing the marker, release your welly.

FLY YOUR FLAGS

Make your summer fête look flagtastic with Great British mini bunting.

You will need

- a pencil
- 10 pieces of paper
- colouring pencils
- scissors
- a stapler
- ribbon.

1. Use a pencil to trace the flags below as many times as you can onto your pieces of paper.

2. Colour in your flags and cut them out.

3. Fold the flag along the dotted line and staple them to the ribbon so they are 5 cm apart.

4. String up your bunting.

GARDEN CRICKET

Grab a bat, some friends and head out into the garden or park to play a game of garden cricket. It's fast and super-easy to learn.

You will need
• cricket bat or tennis racket
• tennis ball or other soft ball
• 3+ players.

1. Decide who will bat and who will bowl first. The rest of the players will be the fielders.

2. The batter must take the bat, walk 5 metres away from the bowler and hold the bat in front of his or her legs. The batter's legs act as the stumps would in real cricket.

3. The batter must stay on the same spot at all times. They're allowed to turn to face the other way but they can't move from the position they first stand in.

4. The bowler throws the ball, underarm or overarm, at the batter's legs and the batter tries to hit it as far as possible. If the bowler hits the batter's legs, the batter is out and it's the bowler's turn to bat.

5. If a fielder or the bowler catches a hit ball, before it touches the ground, they must shout 'How's that!'. It is then their turn to bat. If a fielder or the bowler doesn't catch the ball, they must bowl from where the ball lands.

6. The game continues until you want to stop. The winner is the player who was batting longest.

FESTIVAL FEVER

Rosy, Andrew, Chloe and David are at the main stage at a festival but can't decide where to go next. Can you help them decide?

- Andrew doesn't want to listen to any more music
- Rosy doesn't like clowns
- None of them are hungry or thirsty
- None of them need to wash.

22

WOW-FACTOR WELLIES

Give an old pair of Wellington boots the wow factor and stop the rain from ruining your festival look.

You will need
- Wellington boots
- warm soapy water
- scrubbing brush
- paper
- pencil
- paintbrush
- acrylic paints.

1. Wash your wellies using plenty of warm soapy water. Remove any mud and stones from the soles using a scrubbing brush. Rinse and leave to dry.

2. While your boots dry, plan your design on paper. If your boots are red, you could paint black spots on them to turn them into ladybird boots or if they are green, you could paint on scales and eyes and turn them into a pair of dino boots. Let your imagination run wild.

3. Paint your design onto your boots. Leave them to dry. and wait for the rain!

Great British tip
Why wait for a festival? Put on your new boots and find the nearest puddle.

23

FUNNY MONEY

Pretend to be King or Queen of Great Britain by drawing your face on the banknote and coins below.

Great British tip
The next time you send thank-you notes why not give them the royal treatment and design your own bank notes with your message written on the back?

SAVE THE QUEEN!

Oh no! The Queen has got lost in the maze at her annual garden party. Can you help her find her way out and get back to the palace?

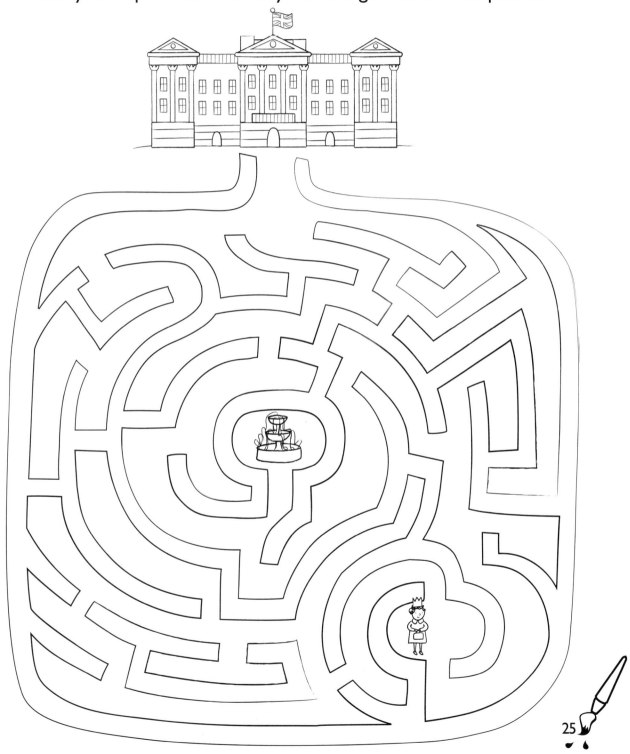

25

CRAZY GOLF

Did you know golf was invented in Scotland?
Create your own course and play a game of mini golf today.

You will need

- colouring pencils
- scissors
- glue
- table-tennis ball
- walking stick or hockey stick.

1. Colour in the shape opposite using any colours that you like. This is called the 'arch'.

2. Carefully cut out the shape.

3. Fold along all of the dotted lines to form the arch.

4. Apply glue to the tabs and then stick your arch together. Leave it to dry.

How to play the game

1. Place your finished arch on the floor and then put a table-tennis ball opposite the hole, around a metre away.

2. The first player must tap the table-tennis ball gently with the walking stick or hockey stick and attempt to get it through the hole. If he/she doesn't manage to get the ball through the hole first time ask him/her to try again.

3. The winner is the player who gets the ball through the hole in the fewest number of tries.

Great British tip
When you've tackled this course, get creative by moving the arch further away, putting it on a ramp of books or adding obstacles.

26

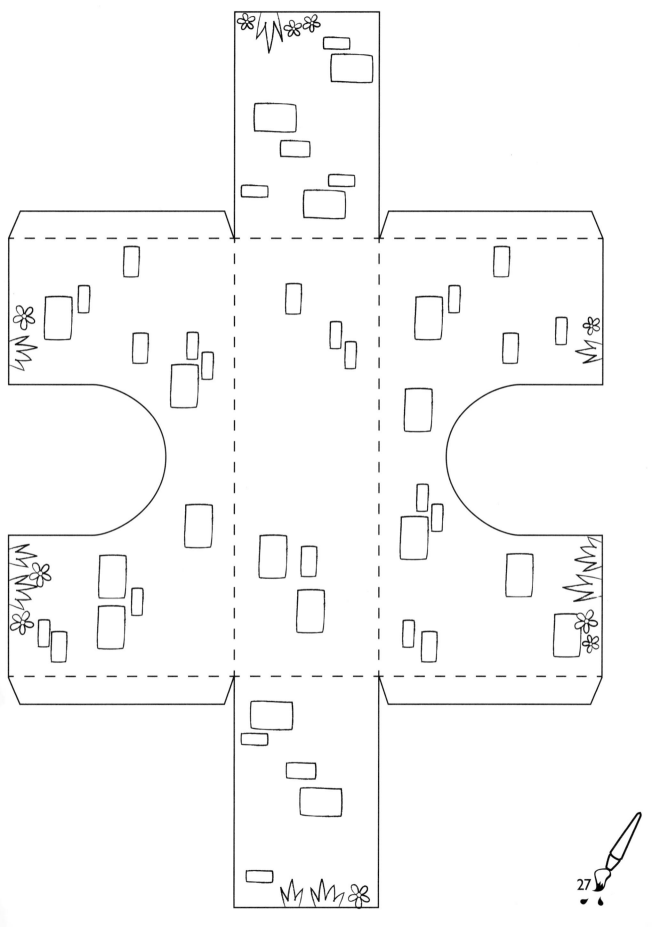

27

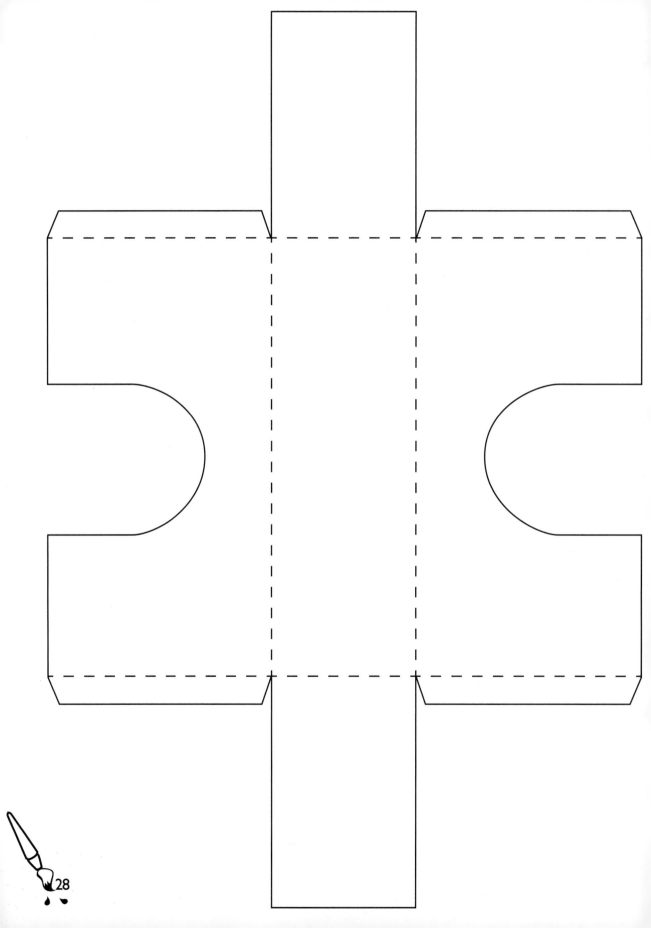

28

IT'S A SHORE THING

Grab your bucket and a net and go rock-pooling. Count how many of each animal you can see hiding in the rock pool.

sea anemones

limpets

starfish

shore crabs

hermit crabs

CARNIVAL COLOURS

It's children's day at the Notting Hill Carnival in London so why not make your own magical mask and join the party?

You will need

- colouring pens or pencils
- scissors
- glue
- glitter
- sequins
- feathers (optional)
- clear hole reinforcements
- a sharp pencil
- modelling clay
- elastic
- sticky tape.

1. Colour in the masks on the opposite page lots of bright colours.

2. Cut them out. Take extra care with the eye holes.

3. Decorate your masks with glitter and sequins and, if you have them, glue feathers to the sides.

4. Ask an adult to make holes in your masks at the places marked, using a sharp pencil and modelling clay.

5. Stick one clear hole reinforcement around each hole.

6. Thread elastic through the holes in the masks and secure with a knot and sticky tape.

7. Put on your mask and your most colourful party clothes. Give your spare mask to a friend.

31

32

IT'S HAMMER TIME

It's time for the Highland Games, Scotland's ultimate test of strength.
Robert, Alex and Aiden have thrown hammers as far as they can.
Follow the paths to find out who threw their hammer furthest.

Robert

Alex

Aiden

CHIP SHOP CHAOS

Oh no! Greg has lost Mrs Richardson's order.
Can you find all the food on her list?

3 x portions of chips
2 x large fish
3 x battered sausages
2 x mushy peas
4 x tomato sauce sachets

MUSHY PEAS

Fish and chips are delicious but they are even nicer with a big spoonful of mushy peas. Next time you know you're having fish and chips for tea why not make your own mushy peas to go with them?

You will need
- 250 g dried, marrowfat peas
- 1 tsp bicarbonate of soda
- water
- salt and pepper.

Warning! *Make sure you ask an adult to help you whenever you'd like to use the hob.*

1. Put the peas and the bicarbonate of soda into a large bowl. Ask an adult to pour over one litre of boiling water and stir.

2. Leave the peas to soak overnight. Make sure that the peas are always covered in water. Add more cool water if you need to.

3. Drain the peas using a colander, and rinse with plenty of fresh water.

4. Put the peas into a saucepan and cover with water.

5. Ask an adult to help you put the pan over a high heat. When the peas start to boil, turn the heat down to simmer them for 30-40 minutes.

6. Give the peas a good stir every five minutes, adding a little more water if they start to stick to the bottom of the pan.

7. Once the peas are soft and mushy, add a pinch of salt, a grind of pepper and serve hot with your fish and chips! Pea-licious!

CONKER CHAMP!

This October find your nearest horse-chestnut tree, follow these instructions and declare yourself conker-fighting champion!

You will need

- shiny round conker
- jar
- 300 ml vinegar
- stopwatch
- baking tray
- metal skewer
- 40 cm of string.

Choose your conker

Remember, fresh is best. Find a green, spiky seed pod under a horse-chestnut tree and ease it open. The perfect conker is round, with no lumps or bumps and glossy, with no marks or cracks on its surface. Collect lots of conkers and choose your favourite.

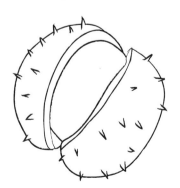

Warning! *Make sure you ask an adult to help you whenever you'd like to use the oven.*

Get battle ready

1. Ask an adult to preheat the oven to 240 °C/gas mark 8.

2. Place the conker in the jar and carefully cover in vinegar. Start your stopwatch. After two minutes, remove the conker from the jar. Wipe away the excess vinegar. Save the vinegar for future conkers.

3. Place your conker on a baking tray and ask an adult to put it in the oven for two minutes, remove and then leave it to cool.

4. Ask an adult to pierce the conker through the middle of the rough pale disc on the top with the metal skewer. Thread your conker onto a piece of string. Tie a double knot in the bottom of the string to keep it in place. Your conker is ready to go!

Great British tip
Experiment by putting your conkers in the vinegar and oven for different lengths of time to discover what works best for you.

The perfect strike
The rules of conkers change throughout Britain, but the basic idea is that two players take turns to swing their conker at their opponent's to try and smash it to smithereens. Follow these tips and you'll be conker champ!

1. If you are right handed, stand facing your opponent with your right foot forward. Reverse these instructions if you are left handed.

2. Wrap the string of your conker around your right hand three times and hold the conker with your left.

3. Study your opponent's conker. Look out for any lumps and bumps on their conker's surface. This is where you want to aim your strike.

4. Pull the conker back until the string is very tight. You should feel the string tightening around your right hand.

5. To make your strike, keep your eye on your opponent's conker. Release your conker from your left hand and drop your right hand down as fast as you can.

6. Once you have damaged your opponent's conker, keep aiming at the damaged spot until it breaks and you can claim your victory.

CONKER CONFUSION

Oh no! Everyone's conkers have become tangled. Can you help them get untangled in time for the match?

Rosy

Liam

B

A

C

D

Arjan

Julie

MYSTERY SPLASH

Join the dots to see who is splashing in the puddle.

39

HOT SAMOSAS

These crispy vegetable samosas are a perfect snack and easy to make.

You will need
- 2 tbsp vegetable oil
- 1 medium onion, chopped
- 2 cm ginger, grated
- 1 tsp mustard seeds
- 100 g frozen peas
- 100 g frozen sweetcorn
- 1 tbsp ground coriander
- 1 tsp ground cumin
- 1 tsp mild chilli powder
- 1 tsp curry powder
- 1 large potato, boiled and cubed
- 1 tbsp lemon juice
- ½ tsp salt
- ½ pack filo pastry
- 50 g melted butter.

1. Ask an adult to preheat the oven to 220 °C/gas mark 7.

2. Ask an adult to help you heat the oil in a small frying pan. When the oil is hot, add the onion, ginger and mustard seeds, and cook until the onions are soft.

3. Add the peas and sweetcorn and give the pan a good stir.

Warning! *Make sure you ask an adult to help you whenever you'd like to use a sharp knife or the oven.*

4. In a bowl, mix the remaining spices and add them to the pan. Stir well before adding the potato, lemon juice and salt. Cook for ten minutes. Leave to cool.

5. Unroll the pastry and cut in half lengthways. Peel off two strips and lay them on top of one another. Cover the rest with a damp tea towel to stop them drying out.

6. Put a tablespoonful of mixture on to one end of the pastry.

7. Take the corner of the pastry and fold it over the mixture.

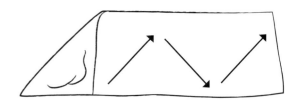

8. Keep folding the pastry over the mixture until you have a triangle-shaped parcel. Cut away any extra pastry. Repeat with the rest of the pastry until you've used all of your mixture.

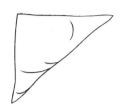

9. Place your samosas on a greased baking tray and brush with melted butter. Ask an adult to put them in the oven for ten minutes or until golden brown.

10. Leave to cool before serving. They go perfectly with a good dollop of mango chutney.

Can you find the ingredients in the list opposite in the wordsearch?

M	C	S	O	E	B	C	R	J	L	U	D	R
W	U	M	T	R	U	O	F	P	E	N	L	E
C	R	S	A	L	T	R	I	N	M	T	I	D
U	R	O	T	S	T	I	L	R	O	D	O	W
M	Y	W	O	A	E	A	O	O	N	S	E	O
I	P	L	P	E	R	N	P	C	J	I	L	P
N	O	I	N	O	G	D	A	T	U	T	B	I
E	W	R	G	F	H	E	S	E	I	T	A	L
L	D	C	B	Z	N	R	T	E	C	L	T	L
Q	E	U	S	A	E	P	R	W	E	I	E	I
C	R	F	I	A	O	L	Y	S	K	D	G	H
D	B	N	U	M	L	A	N	C	W	T	E	C
G	I	N	G	E	R	T	V	R	E	X	V	O

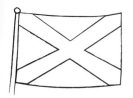 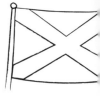

I-SPY SCOTLAND

Put a tick next to each of the things below that you see when you are out and about in Scotland.

Man wearing a kilt ◯   Scottish flag ◯   Sporran ◯

 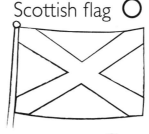 

Highland cattle ◯   Irn Bru ◯   Highland dancer ◯

Haggis ◯   Stag ◯   Loch ◯

  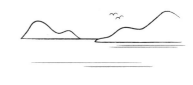

Thistle ◯   Square sausage ◯   Tartan ◯

 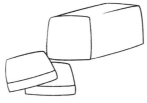

Bagpipes ◯   West Highland terrier ◯   Douglas fir tree ◯

FOSSIL FINDING

Did you know that British beaches are a great place to find fossils?

Where to go?

- Dorset Coast, England
- North Yorkshire Coast, England
- Essex Coast, England
- Sutherland, Scotland
- Llantwit Major, Wales.

What to look for?

- Pick up any stones on the beach that look different or interesting. If any of your stones look like the pictures below, you've found a fossil

Warning! *Tides can change very quickly. Always check the local tide schedule before heading to the shore and take an adult with you.*

- If you see any irregular lumps or swirls on rocks these could be fossilized ammonites or even trilobites – extinct animals without backbones, known as invertebrates

- Look out for large flat areas of rock on the shore and see if you can find a series of regular dents in the stone. These could be dinosaur footprints from millions of years ago.

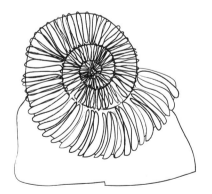

Ammonite

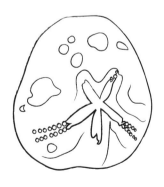

Fossilized sea urchin

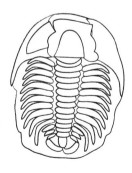

Trilobite

LOCH NESS MONSTER

Celebrate St Andrew's Day, on November 30th, by sculpting Scotland's most mysterious resident – the Loch Ness Monster.

You will need

- self-hardening clay
- table knife
- paint
- paintbrush
- PVA glue
- pair of googly eyes.

1. Take a tennis-ball-sized lump of self-hardening clay and roll it into a sausage shape about 40 cm long.

2. Use a table knife to cut the clay into four equal pieces.

3. Take two of the pieces of clay and bend them into arch shapes. The clay may need to be rolled a little more if it's not long enough.

4. Roll one of the straight pieces into a point and bend it over slightly to make a tail. Take the other piece and bend it over 3 cm to make Nessie's head and neck.

5. Leave your pieces to dry following the directions on the packet of clay.

6. When your clay is dry, paint it. There have never been any official sightings of Nessie so you can paint yours any colour you like. Why not try the colours of the Scottish flag, blue and white? Leave it to dry.

7. To make your Nessie nice and shiny, paint a coat of PVA glue over each piece and leave to dry.

8. Glue the googly eyes on either side of Nessie's head. Leave it to dry. Now you can say you've seen the Loch Ness Monster.

Great British fact
Loch Ness is big! There is more water in Scotland's Loch Ness than there is in all of the other lakes in Great Britain put together. No wonder Nessie is so hard to find!

GREAT BRITISH DEFENDERS

This castle needs defending! Finish drawing the army to keep invaders out. Don't forget to place your army in good defending positions.

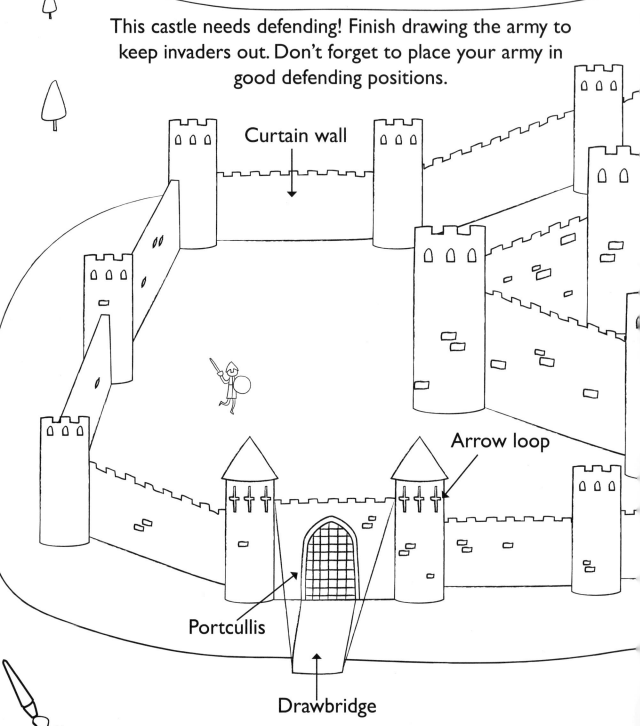

Curtain wall

Arrow loop

Portcullis

Drawbridge

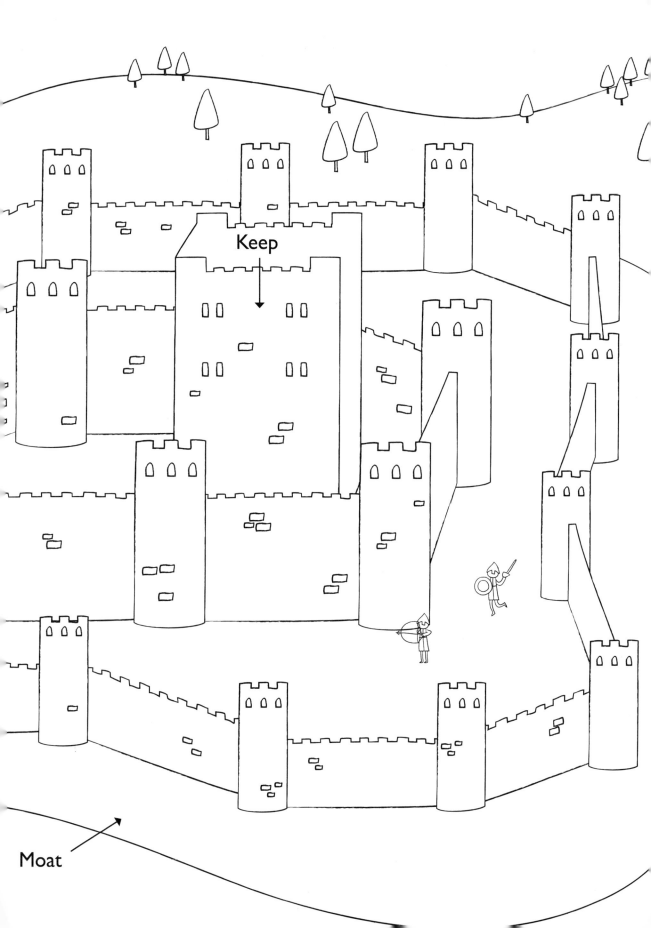

Keep

Moat

BRITISH BRILLIANCE

Over the centuries brilliant inventors from England, Scotland and Wales have done their bit to make Britain great. Can you draw a line from each invention to the correct country?

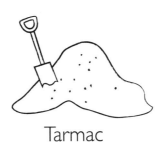

Tarmac

Microphone

Modern toothbrush

Telephone

Wales

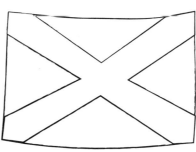

Scotland

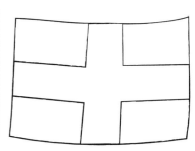

England

The +, - and = signs

Reflecting telescope

Wind-up radio

Television

48

BE A GREAT BRITISH INVENTOR

Why don't you try designing your own invention? Maybe it could be something to help you tidy your room, do your homework for you or how about your own pet robot?

TRIUMPHANT TEAM

Can you spot ten differences between these two team photographs?

THE PENALTY BOX

It takes a real fan to be able to solve this puzzle inspired by Great Britain's favourite game. Fill in the blank squares so that each row and each column only has one item from the sports shop.

REMEMBER, REMEMBER, THE 5TH OF NOVEMBER

It can get cold standing around outside waiting to see the fireworks on bonfire night. Make sure you are warm enough with this bobble hat.

You will need
- pencil
- pair of compasses
- ruler
- I old thin knitted jumper
- I piece of paper
- felt-tip pen
- scissors
- I large needle
- thread
- thin card
- wool.

I. On a piece of paper carefully use a pair of compasses and a ruler to draw a hat shape that's 18 cm wide and 22 cm high at it's highest point. Cut out your template.

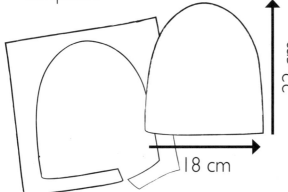

2. Place the template on the jumper so the flat edge of the template lies along the bottom of your jumper. Draw around it using a felt-tip pen. Repeat this so that you have two hat shapes on your jumper. Cut them out.

3. Place your hat shapes on top of one another, with the pattern on the inside.

4. Thread your needle and tie a knot in the end of the thread. Starting at the bottom left corner, 1.5 cm in from the cut edge of your hat shape, push the needle through the fabric and bring it back up and out the other side,

roughly 1 cm from where you went in. Repeat this until you get to the bottom right corner, and tie a knot in the end of your thread. Leave the bottom edge open.

5. Turn your hat inside out so that your stitches are on the inside.

6. To make a pompom template, set your compasses to 3 cm and draw a circle on a piece of card. Then set them to 6 cm and draw another circle from the same centre point to make a doughnut shape. Do this twice.

8. Place one ring on top of the other and wrap the wool around the rings several times until you can no longer pass any

any wool through the hole in the centre.

9. Trim the wool around the edge of the ring until you see the card inside. Carefully insert your scissors between the two pieces of card and cut all the way around the outside.

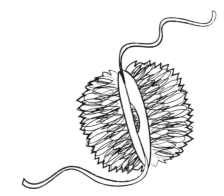

10. Push a piece of wool between the two pieces of card, wrap it around the centre twice and secure with a knot.

11. Pull away the card rings and fluff up your pompom. Secure it to the top of your hat using a few stitches.

SPLASH OF COLOUR

Rainbows aren't the only brightly coloured things that a good shower can make. The next time the clouds gather get creative with this unique gift wrap.

You will need
- empty salt and pepper pots
- powder paints
- newspaper
- a tray
- thick absorbent paper.

1. Unscrew the tops of the salt and pepper pots and fill each pot with a different colour of powder paint. Screw the tops back on.

2. Lay some newspaper down on the floor near your front or back door. Put your tray on the newspaper and place the piece of absorbent paper onto the tray.

3. Shake your pots over your paper to cover them with a light dusting of powder paint.

4. Put on your raincoat, carefully lift up the tray and take it outside. Lay your tray somewhere flat where it will get a good shower of rain. Leave it out in the rain for ten minutes.

5. Bring in your paper, lay it on some fresh newspaper and leave to dry. Save the paper to make a present look extra special. You can even make gift tags out of it.

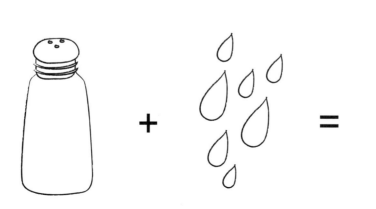

I-SPY WALES

Put a tick next to each of the things below that you spy when you are out and about in Wales.

Welsh flag ◯

A Welsh dresser ◯
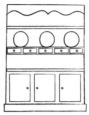

Welsh cakes ◯

A sign written in Welsh ◯

A daffodil ◯

Traditional Welsh dress ◯

A love spoon ◯

A leek

Mount Snowdon

Welsh rarebit

A rugby match

Caerphilly cheese ◯

A dragon ◯

A castle ◯

Sheep farm ◯

56

DRAGON QUEST

Can you complete the dragon quest and find all six dragons hiding in this valley?

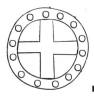
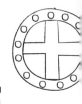

THE KNIGHTS OF THE ROUND TABLE

Only the bravest knights were invited to sit at King Arthur's Round Table. Make your own shield so you can join them.

You will need

- large cardboard box
- a pencil
- scissors
- newspaper
- paints
- paintbrush
- ruler
- masking tape.

1. Use your pencil to draw a large shield shape on the side of your cardboard box. Cut it out.

2. Lay your shield on newspaper and paint it any way you like. How about a fierce dragon or lion on the front to scare your opponent? Paint the back. Leave to dry.

3. To make an arm loop for your shield: cut a strip of cardboard measuring 10 cm x 30 cm.

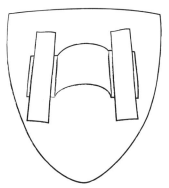

4. Bend your cardboard in a loop, like the diagram above, and stick the sides to the back of your shield using masking tape.

5. Put on your shield and get ready to face your foe in battle.

WHICH KNIGHT IS RIGHT?

Can you find the famous knight Sir Gawain from the clues below?

1. Sir Gawain's shield doesn't have a cross on it
2. He has a round shield with lions on it
3. He has a pointy helmet
4. His visor is up.

Can you also find two identical knights?

GREAT BRITISH STREET PARTY

Everyone loves having a street party. How many English, Scottish, Welsh and British flags can you see? Colour them in as you count them.

ALL THE ANSWERS

Spot the Difference page 3

Munro Mayhem page 15

Festival Fever page 22

Rosy, Andrew, Chloe and David decided to go to the Poetry tent.

Save the Queen page 25

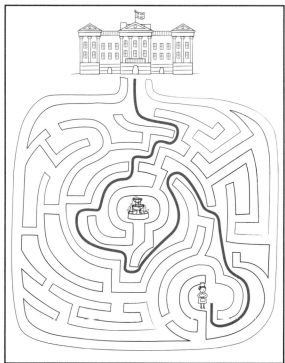

It's a Shore Thing page 29

There are five sea anemones, ten limpets, three starfish, three shore crabs and two hermit crabs.

It's Hammer Time page 33

Chip Shop Chaos page 34

Conker Confusion page 38
Rosy: **A**, Liam: **C**, Arjan: **D**, Julie: **B**.

Mystery Splash page 39
It's a frog, enjoying the rain!

Hot Samosas page 41

M	C	S	O	E	B	C	R	J	L	U	D	R
W	U	M	T	R	U	O	F	P	E	N	L	E
C	R	S	A	L	T	R	I	N	M	T	I	D
U	R	O	T	S	T	I	L	R	O	D	O	W
M	Y	W	O	A	E	A	O	N	S	E	O	O
I	P	L	P	E	R	N	P	C	J	I	L	P
N	O	I	N	O	G	D	A	T	U	T	B	I
E	W	R	G	F	H	E	S	E	I	T	A	L
L	D	C	B	Z	N	R	T	E	C	L	T	L
Q	E	U	S	A	E	P	R	W	E	I	E	I
C	R	F	I	A	O	L	Y	S	K	D	G	H
D	B	N	U	M	L	A	N	C	W	T	E	C
G	I	N	G	E	R	T	V	R	E	X	V	O

British Brilliance page 48
Welsh inventions
Microphone by David Edward Hughes
The +, - and = signs by Robert Recorde

Scottish inventions
Television by John Logie Baird
Tarmac by John MacAdam
Telephone by Alexander Graham Bell

English inventions
Wind-up radio by Trevor Baylis
Reflecting telescope by Isaac Newton
Modern toothbrush by William Addis

Triumphant Team page 50

The Penalty Box page 51

🧢	🧤	⚽	👟	🧢
⚽	🧢	🧢	🧤	👟
👟	🧢	🧤	🧢	⚽
🧢	⚽	👟	🧢	🧤
🧤	👟	🧢	⚽	🧢

Dragon Quest page 57

Which Knight is Right? page 59

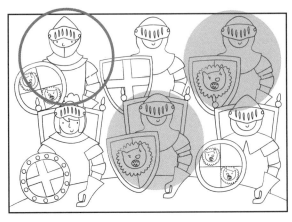

Great British Street Party page 60 and 61
There are ten British flags, ten Scottish flags, nine English flags and eight Welsh flags.

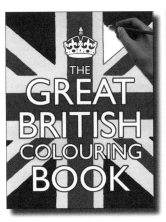

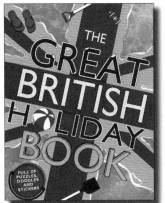

**ALSO
AVAILABLE**

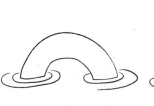